WHAT NOW, CHARLIE BROWN?

by Charles M. Schulz

Selected Cartoons from
The Unsinkable Charlie Brown, Vol. 1

A FAWCETT CREST BOOK

Fawcett Publications, Inc., Greenwich, Conn.

WHAT NOW, CHARLIE BROWN?

This book, prepared especially for Fawcett Publications, Inc.,
comprises the first half of *THE UNSINKABLE CHARLIE
BROWN,* and is reprinted by arrangement with Holt, Rinehart &
Winston, Inc.

Printed in the United States of America
May 1972

WELL, DON'T JUST STAND THERE...
GO GET A SHOVEL, AND HELP ME!

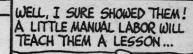

AUGH!

NEVER SET YOUR STOMACH FOR A JELLY-BREAD SANDWICH UNTIL YOU'RE SURE THERE'S SOME JELLY!

SCHULZ

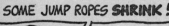

WELL, I LEARNED SOMETHING ABOUT JUMPING ROPE IN THE RAIN....

SOME JUMP ROPES **SHRINK**!

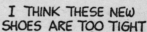

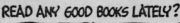

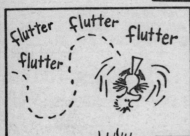

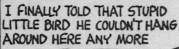

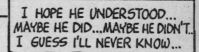

YOUR SWEETIE IS BACK!

SCHULZ

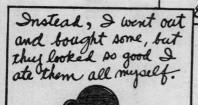

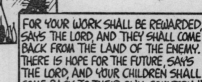

NOW, I THINK NO ONE WILL DENY THAT SPIRIT PLAYS AN IMPORTANT ROLE IN WINNING BALL GAMES..

SOME MIGHT SAY THAT IT PLAYS THE MOST IMPORTANT ROLE..

THE DESIRE TO WIN IS WHAT MAKES A TEAM GREAT..WINNING IS EVERYTHING!

THE ONLY THING THAT MATTERS IS TO COME IN FIRST PLACE!

WHAT I'M TRYING TO SAY IS THAT NO ONE EVER REMEMBERS WHO COMES IN SECOND PLACE!

I DO, CHARLIE BROWN... IN 1928, THE GIANTS AND PHILADELPHIA FINISHED SECOND. IN 1929, IT WAS PITTSBURGH AND THE YANKEES..IN 1930, IT WAS CHICAGO AND WASHINGTON..IN 1931, IT WAS THE GIANTS AND THE YANKEES..IN 1932, IT WAS PITTSBURGH AND...

AND ANOTHER GREAT SEASON GETS UNDERWAY!

SCHULZ

I DON'T KNOW ABOUT THIS NEXT BATTER, CHARLIE BROWN..HE'S PRETTY GOOD..

THAT'S RIGHT, CHARLIE BROWN.. YOU'D BETTER WATCH HIM..

WELL, WHAT DO YOU THINK? SHALL I GIVE HIM THE OL' CHANGE OF PACE? THE LET-UP?

NO, HE'D KILL IT, CHARLIE BROWN...JUST GIVE HIM FAST ONES, BUT KEEP THEM LOW..

THIS GUY SAYS FOR ME TO TELL YOU THAT IF YOU THROW ANYTHING THAT EVEN **LOOKS** LIKE IT MIGHT BE A BEAN-BALL, HE'S GOING TO COME OUT HERE AND POUND YOU RIGHT INTO THE GROUND!

YOU SAY YOU MET THIS LINUS KID AT CAMP?

YES, AND THE YEAR BEFORE I MET A FRIEND OF HIS NAMED CHARLIE BROWN..

HE WAS A STRANGE ROUND-HEADED KID WHO NEVER TALKED ABOUT ANYTHING EXCEPT BASEBALL AND THIS AWFUL TEAM OF HIS THAT ALWAYS LOSES...

I LOVE BASEBALL! GET ON THE PHONE, QUICK! TELL HIM YOUR FRIEND, "PEPPERMINT" PATTY, HAS VOLUNTEERED TO HELP!

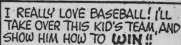

I REALLY LOVE BASEBALL! I'LL TAKE OVER THIS KID'S TEAM, AND SHOW HIM HOW TO **WIN**!!

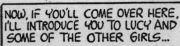

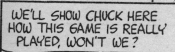

NOW Peanuts Jewelry

Each item is 14 Kt. gold finish, hand-crafted cloisonné in brilliant colors, exquisitely designed by Aviva. Items shown in actual size. Complete satisfaction guaranteed or money refunded.

No. 10 pin $3

No. 11 pin $3

No. 12 pin $3

No. 13A pierced $3
No. 13B
non-pierced $3

No. 14 pin $3

No. 15 pin $3.

No. 16 pin $3

No. 17A pierced $3
No. 17B
non-pierced $3

No. 18 pin $3

No. 19 pin $3

No. 20 pin $3

© United Feature Syndicate, Inc. 1971

No. 21 pin $3

More Peanuts Jewelry
See Previous Page·

No. 22 tie tack $3

No. 23 tie tack $3

No. 24 key chain $3

No. 25 money clip $4

No. 26 tie tack $3

No. 27 tie bar $3

No. 28 cufflinks $4

No. 29 pin $3

Please specify identity number of each item ordered and add 25¢ for each item to cover postage and handling. Personal check or money order. No cash. Send orders to HAMILTON HOUSE, Cos Cob, Conn. 06807.

© United Feature Syndicate, inc. 1971